FIGURATIVE LANGUAGE

Table of Contents

Introduction

Most of the elementary curriculum today is aimed at a literal education—adding numbers, remembering facts. Little of the curriculum deals with critical thinking: interpreting, analyzing, using abstract or figurative language. This book, *Figurative Language*, attempts to promote practice in critical thinking. The students must learn to recognize figurative devices that yield a secondary level of meaning.

A variety of lessons and activities gives students practice in literal and figurative thought. They make literal comparisons to learn logical relationships.

Then, they move on to figurative comparisons, in which the relationships are more abstract. The students are also exposed to poetic devices. Finally, the students study homographs and homophones, seeing that words can be fun to work with.

This book is divided into three units.

- Unit 1 covers the concepts of literal and figurative language, with particular emphasis on analogies, similes, and metaphors.

- Unit 2 covers the application of those concepts, as students distinguish between literal and figurative language and identify figurative devices.

- Unit 3 provides enrichment activities, in which the students use language to solve riddles and make jokes. All the units stress a higher level of thought and provide many writing activities.

At the first of the book is a general assessment. It can be used before the students begin the activities to determine a benchmark. The assessment can then be used after the activities have been completed to gauge students' progress. At the end of many activities is a "More to Do" section. This section invites the students to use the concepts they have learned to create their own works.

As a final note, be aware that there are several instances of misused words in this book, especially in Unit 3. These misused words are meant to demonstrate the playful nature of language.

Teaching Figurative Language

Literal comparisons, which are often called analogies, provide the students with a form of critical thinking. They must recognize the important relationship between the part and the whole, and they must also recognize the relationships between sets of objects. This book provides practice in making literal comparisons.

The most important aspect of teaching figurative language is enabling the students to see that the author is saying two things at once. One of the levels is always literal.

The man ran across the street.

This example uses nouns, verbs, and prepositions to describe an action literally. The second level of meaning is figurative.

The man ran across the street <u>like a frightened cat.</u>

The simile in the second example gives the reader two images to consider, and a comparison is made between the two. One is like the other. Ask the students if they have ever seen a frightened cat move. If they have, they know more about how the man ran across the street. The students' understanding of the figurative example depends on their level of experience. Figurative devices, therefore, require the input of the reader, unlike the multiplication tables, which are a matter of rote.

Unlike in literal comparisons, though, in most figures of speech (similes, metaphors, etc.), only one of the elements is literal, or concrete. The other element is usually figurative, or abstract. In figurative devices, authors often compare a more unknown quality or value (abstract) to a common thing (concrete). Robert Burns wrote long ago, "My love is like a red, red rose." If the students understand the qualities of a rose, they can enhance their understanding of love. So always point the students to the comparison being made, to the terms being compared, and to their own feelings about what the comparison means.

Figurative language, of course, is a hard subject to grade quantitatively. An assessment is included in this book, but it only gauges the more basic aspects of figurative language. Students must identify a simile or complete a comparison. The true thrust of teaching (and assessing) figurative language should be qualitative. Have the students discuss and write figurative language. The minds of young students are like undiscovered treasure mines.

Assessment

✏️

DIRECTIONS |||| **Read the following sentences. Decide if each sentence uses literal or figurative language. Write *literal* or *figurative* on the line.**

_____ **1.** The backpack had many books in it.

_____ **2.** The backpack was as heavy as an elephant.

_____ **3.** The man was a monster to work for.

_____ **4.** The dog ran like the wind across the playground.

_____ **5.** The cow walked slowly along the road.

_____ **6.** The volcano erupted in the dark night.

DIRECTIONS |||| **Choose words from the WORD BOX to complete the analogies. Not all the words in the box will be used.**

WORD BOX

snake	hot	orange	small	nests	pig
smell	dark	young	caboose	ear	track

7. <u>Houses</u> are to <u>people</u> **AS** _____ are to <u>birds</u>.

8. <u>Peel</u> is to _____ **AS** <u>skin</u> is to <u>apple</u>.

9. <u>Teeth</u> are to <u>dog</u> **AS** <u>fangs</u> are to _____.

10. <u>Hear</u> is to _____ **AS** <u>see</u> is to <u>eye</u>.

11. <u>Day</u> is to <u>night</u> **AS** _____ is to <u>cold</u>.

12. <u>Glad</u> is to <u>bad</u> **AS** <u>big</u> is to _____.

13. <u>Road</u> is to <u>car</u> **AS** _____ is to <u>train</u>.

14. <u>Big</u> is to _____ **AS** <u>old</u> is to <u>new</u>.

Go on to the next page.

Assessment, p. 2

| DIRECTIONS ||||| **Circle the letter of the homograph whose meaning fits both sentences.**

15. I _____ a great program last night.
You need a _____ to cut that board.
  a. heard
  b. scissors
  c. saw
  d. attended

16. That table is so _____ that it's easy to lift.
Please turn on the _____.
  a. radio
  b. beautiful
  c. narrow
  d. light

| DIRECTIONS ||||| **Choose the correct homophone in ( ) to complete each sentence.**

17. At the end of the _____, Bob made a plan. (weak, week)

18. The store was easy to _____. (find, fined)

19. His heart _____ faster. (beet, beat)

20. From the hilltop, Meg could _____ her house. (see, sea)

| DIRECTIONS ||||| **Read the following poem. Find the similes and the metaphor in the poem. Draw a line under the similes. Draw a circle around the metaphor.**

Mama Is a Sunrise
by Evelyn Tooley Hunt

When she comes slip-footing through the door,
  she kindles us
  like lump coal lighted,
  and we wake up glowing.
She puts a spark even in Papa's eyes
and turns out all our darkness.

When she comes sweet-talking in the room,
  she warms us
  like grits and gravy,
  and we rise up shining.
Even at night-time Mama is a sunrise
that promises tomorrow and tomorrow.

Say What You Mean!

Language helps us to communicate. With language, we can write and read, talk and sing, think and imagine. But language can be confusing, too. Some words are hard to say. Some words are hard to spell. Some words are spelled alike but mean different things. Some words sound alike but are spelled differently and mean different things.

Language can have different levels of meaning, too. Some words are **literal language**. This type of language is sometimes called **concrete language**. Literal language means saying exactly what you mean. Literal or concrete words have an exact meaning. They are not exaggerated. They allow the reader to see a clear mental picture, or **image**. *Car* is a literal word. You can see a clear picture of a car in your mind.

Another kind of language is **figurative language**. Figurative language gives a meaning that is not exactly that of the words used. Figurative language tries to create a clearer mental picture, or image, for you. The image helps you to understand the writing better. For example, *Mother Nature* is a figurative expression. Nature is suggested to be a caring, protective mother.

DIRECTIONS ‖‖ **Read the three passages below. Two use figurative language, and one uses literal language. See if you can figure out which two use figurative language. Circle the two passages that use figurative language.**

Paul Bunyan was huge. In fact, he was so huge that he used a pitchfork to comb his hair and a push broom to brush his teeth.

Paul Bunyan tall tales, or legends, exaggerate to make Paul and the things he does seem bigger and better than they really are. This kind of figurative language is known as exaggeration.

The gentle breeze whispered good morning to each new day, as the flowers opened their petals to the rising sun.

Remember: Literal language means what it says. Figurative language tries to give you a picture of what is happening.

Go on to the next page.

Say What You Mean!, p. 2

DIRECTIONS |||| **Read the following sentences. Underline the sentence if it is an example of figurative language. Circle the sentence if it is an example of literal language.**

1. Jonathan loves to play with his action figures.

2. After the blizzard, the snowpile was as big as all outdoors.

3. The volcano coughed up ashes, as tears of molten lava ran down the mountainside.

4. My mother and I go to the library every Saturday.

DIRECTIONS |||| **Read the following passage. Then, answer the questions.**

Paul Bunyan was huge. He was as big as a tree. He was so big that he stood sixty feet tall in his stocking feet. Paul's logging camp was also gigantic. The cookhouse was so big inside that it would take a person two days to walk its length.

5. Is the passage about Paul Bunyan literal or figurative? _____

6. Paul Bunyan's size is exaggerated. Write a phrase or a sentence from the passage that contains an example of exaggeration about his size.

_____

_____

7. What words in the passage tell that the cookhouse was a large building? Write them below.

_____

_____

✎✎✎ **MORE TO DO** ✎✎✎

Write one sentence that uses figurative language and one that uses literal language.

_____

_____

_____

_____

Comparisons

A comparison shows how things are alike. A comparison helps you to see how things are related. One kind of comparison is called an **analogy**. An analogy is a way to compare word meanings. An analogy has two parts. The two parts are linked with the word *as*. *As* means "in the same way."

Hat is to head **AS** shoe is to ?

To solve an analogy:

1. Think about how the terms in the first part are related.

   "A hat is worn on the head."

2. Then, think how this relationship works in the second part.

   "Where is a shoe worn?"

A shoe is worn on the foot. So, hat is to head **AS** shoe is to foot.

DIRECTIONS |||| **Choose words from the WORD BOX to complete these analogies. Not all the words in the box will be used.**

WORD BOX

mother	egg	uncle	snow
brother	rooster	sunshine	kitten

1. Mother is to father **AS** aunt is to _____.

2. Dog is to puppy **AS** cat is to _____.

3. Cow is to milk **AS** hen is to _____.

4. Summer is to rain **AS** winter is to _____.

5. Man is to father **AS** woman is to _____.

7

Parts of a Whole

✐✐

Some analogies compare parts of a thing to the whole thing. To figure out the analogy, look for clues in the first part.

<u>Toe</u> is to <u>foot</u> **AS** <u>finger</u> is to ?

Remember, to solve an analogy:

1. Think about how the terms in the first part are related.

   "A toe is part of a foot."

2. Then, think how this relationship works in the second part.

   "What is a finger a part of?"

A finger is part of a hand. So, <u>toe</u> is to <u>foot</u> **AS** <u>finger</u> is to <u>hand</u>.

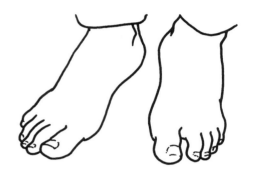

[DIRECTIONS] ‖‖ **Choose words from the WORD BOX to complete these analogies. Not all the words in the box will be used.**

WORD BOX

| tennis | bicycle | leg | tusks |
| feathers | neck | beaks | noise |

1. <u>Hand</u> is to <u>arm</u> **AS** <u>foot</u> is to _____.

2. <u>Steering wheel</u> is to <u>car</u> **AS** <u>handlebars</u> are to _____.

3. <u>Scales</u> are to <u>fish</u> **AS** _____ are to <u>birds</u>.

4. <u>Club</u> is to <u>golf</u> **AS** <u>racket</u> is to _____.

5. <u>Antlers</u> are to <u>deer</u> **AS** _____ are to <u>elephants</u>.

✐✑✐ **MORE TO DO** ✑✐✑

Write your own analogies that show a relationship of a part to the whole. Try to write at least three analogies. Share your analogies with your classmates.

Keep It Moving!

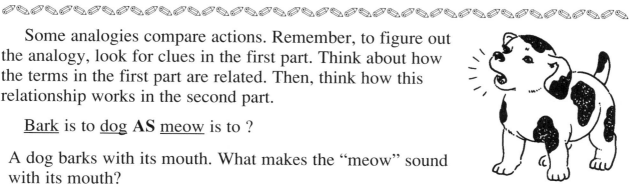

Some analogies compare actions. Remember, to figure out the analogy, look for clues in the first part. Think about how the terms in the first part are related. Then, think how this relationship works in the second part.

Bark is to dog AS meow is to ?

A dog barks with its mouth. What makes the "meow" sound with its mouth?

DIRECTIONS ||||| **Complete the analogies.**

1. Nose is to smell AS eye is to _____.

2. Throw is to hand AS _____ is to foot.

3. Bird is to fly AS frog is to _____.

4. Red is to stop AS green is to _____.

5. Moo is to cow AS _____ is to duck.

6. Pencil is to draw AS _____ is to paint.

7. Beach is to swim AS restaurant is to _____.

8. Sniff is to nose AS wink is to _____.

9. Snake is to bite AS _____ is to sting.

10. Driver is to bus AS pilot is to _____.

✐✎✐ **MORE TO DO** ✎✐✎

Write your own analogies that compare actions. Try to write at least three analogies. For a fun twist, draw pictures instead of using words in your analogies. Share your analogies with your classmates. See if they can figure out your analogies.

Opposites

✏✏✏✏✏✏✏✏✏✏✏✏✏✏✏✏✏✏✏✏✏✏✏✏✏✏✏✏✏✏✏✏✏✏✏✏✏✏

Some analogies compare opposites. Remember, to figure out the analogy, look for clues in the first part. Think about how the terms in the first part are related. Then, think how this relationship works in the second part.

Sometimes, a word in the first part of the analogy is missing. Then, you have to look for clues in the second part.

<u>Sun</u> is to ? **AS** <u>Moon</u> is to <u>night</u>.

The Moon shines at night. When does the Sun shine?

| DIRECTIONS ||||| **Complete the analogies.**

1. <u>Hard</u> is to <u>soft</u> **AS** <u>wet</u> is to _____.

2. <u>Hot</u> is to _____ **AS** <u>fire</u> is to <u>ice</u>.

3. <u>Over</u> is to <u>under</u> **AS** _____ is to <u>far</u>.

4. <u>Tall</u> is to <u>short</u> **AS** <u>thick</u> is to _____.

5. _____ is to <u>small</u> **AS** <u>loud</u> is to <u>quiet</u>.

6. <u>Left</u> is to <u>right</u> **AS** _____ is to <u>wrong</u>.

7. <u>Sharp</u> is to <u>dull</u> **AS** <u>happy</u> is to _____.

8. <u>Hot</u> is to <u>cold</u> **AS** _____ is to <u>cool</u>.

9. <u>Day</u> is to _____ **AS** <u>light</u> is to <u>dark</u>.

10. <u>Up</u> is to _____ **AS** _____ is to <u>out</u>.

✏✏✏ **MORE TO DO** ✏✏✏

Can you write your own analogies that compare opposites? There are many other kinds of analogies to write, too. How many different kinds can you think of? Try to write at least three different kinds of analogies. Share your analogies with your classmates. How many of your analogies can your classmates guess?

Name _____ Date _____

Simile or Metaphor?

What does it mean to compare things? It means to tell how two or more things are alike. Figurative language uses **figures of speech**. These figures of speech are kinds of comparisons. Two figures of speech in this book are similes and metaphors. What two things are compared in the following sentence?

The girl ran from the bees <u>like a frightened cat</u>.

If you said that the <u>running girl</u> and the <u>frightened cat</u> are being compared, you are right! The sentence gives you two images to think about. Have you ever seen a frightened cat move? If you have, you have a better idea about how the girl ran. The clue word *like* is used to make this comparison. When *like* or *as* is used to compare two things, the comparison is called a **simile**.

Sometimes a comparison is made by speaking of one thing as if it were another. This is called a **metaphor**. Metaphors compare things that are not very similar. The following sentence is a metaphor.

Chuck is a racehorse.

In this case, the boy is compared to a racehorse. The metaphor does not mean that Chuck is literally a horse. Perhaps Chuck is a very fast runner. The metaphor compares Chuck's speed to a racehorse's speed. Notice that *like* or *as* is not used.

| DIRECTIONS |||| **In each sentence below, underline the two things being compared. Then, identify the comparison as a *simile* or *metaphor*.**

1. His smile was like sunshine. _____

2. His announcement was a bombshell. _____

3. Sheila acted like a monster. _____

4. My brother is a clown. _____

5. He was busy as a beaver. _____

11

It's As Easy As Pie

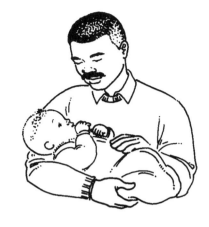

> **To Recognize Similes and Metaphors in Comparisons:**
>
> 1. **READ** the sentence carefully.
> 2. **THINK** what things are being compared.
> 3. **LOOK** for the use of *like* or *as* to signal a simile.
> 4. **NOTICE** if unlike things are compared to signal a metaphor.

DIRECTIONS ||||| **Read each comparison, and answer the questions.**

The baby is an angel.

1. What two things are being compared? _____

_____

2. Is this a simile or metaphor? _____

_____

The thick grass was like carpet under our feet.

3. What two things are being compared? _____

_____

4. Is this a simile or metaphor? _____

_____

The room was an oven.

5. What two things are being compared? _____

_____

6. Is this a simile or metaphor? _____

_____

Poems

Poems are written by **poets**. Poets use many kinds of figurative language. Poets like to play with language. They put words together carefully to make the most sense. They create beautiful pictures with their words.

Poets use rhyming words, or **rhymes**, in their poems. Rhyming words are words that sound similar. Rhymes are often used at the ends of lines in a poem. Poets also use **rhythm**. Rhythm makes the words of the poem sound better. The poem has a "beat." One kind of beat, or **meter**, sounds like the human heartbeat.

A line in the poem may use **alliteration**. Alliteration is when the beginning sounds of words are alike. Many tongue-twisters use alliteration.

The dark duck dropped into the dirty drainpipe.

Here, the "d" sound is repeated.

| DIRECTIONS ||||| **Read the following poem. Draw lines between words that rhyme. Draw a line under words that use alliteration. Circle the similes. Mark an X on the metaphor.**

I like Little Monkey,

I want you to know.

He's like a good buddy,

And he goes where I go.

Little Monkey's a clown—

A fine fellow for all that—

But I wish he did not

Look like a hat!

✐✎✐ MORE TO DO ✐✎✐

Add another verse or two to this poem. What else might Little Monkey look like? He's a pretty funny-looking guy! Try to use all the poet's tools when you write your poem. Include rhyme and rhythm, similes, and alliteration, if you can.

Name _____ Date _____

At Home with Homographs

Homographs are words that are spelled the same but that have different meanings. The words may also be pronounced differently. *Tear*, meaning "to rip," and *tear*, meaning "a water drop from the eye," are homographs.

My mother likes to play the card game of <u>bridge</u>.
The cars drove across the <u>bridge</u>.

The teacher told us to <u>clip</u> the pictures from the magazine.
We used a paper <u>clip</u> to hold the pictures together.

| DIRECTIONS |||| **Circle the letter of the homograph whose meaning fits both sentences.**

1. Use a key to _____ the door.
She saved a _____ of the
    baby's hair.
  a. curl
  b. lock
  c. open
  d. piece

2. I _____ come with you this
    afternoon.
Open the _____ of food for
    the dog.
  a. will
  b. should
  c. bag
  d. can

3. Fill the cereal _____ with milk.
Did you ever _____ on
    Jack's team?
  a. jar
  b. bowl
  c. swim
  d. dish

4. Manny is a big hockey _____.
Turn on the _____! It's hot in here.
  a. fan
  b. radio
  c. player
  d. light

| DIRECTIONS |||| **Write a homograph for each pair of meanings below. The first letter of each word is given.**

5. a. sound made with the fingers   S _____
   b. a metal fastener

6. a. a tree covering   b _____
   b. sound a dog makes

7. a. to press flat   S _____
   b. a yellow vegetable

8. a. place for money   b _____
   b. side of a river

Unit One: Concepts
Figurative Language 4, SV 2718-9

Name _____ Date _____

Answer the Homophone!

Homophones are words that sound the same but are spelled differently. They also have different meanings. *Pair*, *pear*, and *pare* are homophones. Be careful with homophones. If you write the wrong homophone, you may not be saying what you mean. Is this sentence correct?

Wood you like to sea a grate movie?

DIRECTIONS |||| **Complete each sentence correctly. Choose the correct homophone in ( ), and write it in the blank.**

1. I planted a _____ in my garden. (flour, flower)

2. I can't go to school because I have the _____. (flu, flew)

3. Can you untie the _____ in the shoelace? (not, knot)

4. He had heard the strange sound

   _____ times. (to, too, two)

5. The man _____ his horse

   down the _____. (road, rode)

6. Do you _____ the

   _____ home? (no, know; way, weigh)

DIRECTIONS |||| **Think of a homophone for each of these words. Write it on the line next to the word.**

7. seam _____   8. week _____

9. their _____   10. for _____

Unit One: Concepts
Figurative Language 4, SV 2718-9

Alike or Different?

Homographs are words that are spelled the same but that have different meanings. The words may also be pronounced differently. *Bear*, meaning "a big mammal," and *bear*, meaning "to carry," are homographs.

Homophones are words that sound the same but are spelled differently. They also have different meanings. *Hair* and *hare* are homophones.

DIRECTIONS |||| **Circle the letter of the homograph whose meaning fits both sentences.**

1. Put the folder in the _____ cabinet.
Use a nail _____ on your fingernails.
  a. brown
  b. tall
  c. brush
  d. file

2. The _____ flew into its nest.
Jed _____ into the pool headfirst.
  a. bird
  b. ran
  c. dove
  d. jumped

DIRECTIONS |||| **Think of a homophone for each of these words. Write in on the line next to the word.**

3. loan _____

4. our _____

5. allowed _____

6. yoke _____

7. mane _____

8. hole _____

9. rode _____

10. peace _____

✎✎✎ **MORE TO DO** ✎✎✎
Have a contest with your classmates to see who can make the longest list of homophones. The winner should win a grate pries.

He Ate How Much?

Read these two sentences. Think about what they mean.

1. The baby's smile was as wide as the ocean.
2. The baby had a big smile on its face.

How are these two sentences alike? Yes, they are both talking about a baby's big smile. How are they different? The first one uses **figurative language**. Could the baby's smile be as wide as the ocean? Of course not. The author has exaggerated how big the baby's smile is in order to make the sentence more interesting.

The second sentence is an example of **literal language**. The sentence means just what it says. The first one doesn't literally mean what it says.

To Tell the Difference Between Figurative and Literal Language:

1. **READ** the sentence carefully.
2. **THINK** about the meaning of the sentence.
3. **DECIDE** if the sentence means just what it says (literal), or if the sentence has exaggerated what it means (figurative).

DIRECTIONS |||| **Read the following sentences. Decide if they are using figurative or literal language. Write *literal* or *figurative* on the line.**

_____ **1.** David ate a ton of food for lunch.

_____ **2.** David ate a big lunch.

_____ **3.** The woman had a long neck.

_____ **4.** The woman's neck was as long as a giraffe's.

_____ **5.** The news hit us like a bomb.

_____ **6.** The news was very upsetting to us.

_____ **7.** Tina is a monster when she gets mad.

_____ **8.** Tina is hard to get along with when she gets mad.

_____ **9.** The building was so tall it touched the sky.

_____ **10.** The building was very tall.

What You Really Mean Is

DIRECTIONS |||| **Each of the following sentences is an example of figurative language. Write a literal sentence below each sentence to tell what the sentence really means.**

1. John had been in the pool forever.

_____

2. Mother carries everything but the kitchen sink in her purse.

_____

3. When Tom speaks, you can hear him a mile away.

_____

4. Elsie turns into a fish when she gets into the water.

_____

5. Carl's brain must have been on the Moon when he said that.

_____

6. As the plane went higher, the people on the ground turned into ants.

_____

7. The man was as skinny as a rail.

_____

8. It takes an army to wake Bob up.

_____

9. Karen was beginning to melt from the heat.

_____

10. I jumped out of my skin when Doug scared me.

_____

Unit Two: Applications
Figurative Language 4, SV 2718-9

Name _____   Date _____

Finding Similes

Figurative language uses **figures of speech**. One figure of speech is the **simile**. A simile is a comparison of two things that are not usually thought to be alike. A simile uses the clue words *like* or *as* to make the comparison. For example, a simile would be, "The boy ran <u>like</u> a flash of lightning." The simile compares the boy's running to a flash of lightning.

Similes use the words *like* or *as* to show the comparison. But be careful. Not all sentences that have the word *like* contain a simile. For example, "I do not <u>like</u> cats" is not a simile.

DIRECTIONS |||| **Underline the similes in the following poem.**

Little Monkey is a funny guy.

Sometimes he buzzes like a fly.

Sometimes he barks like a hungry dog.

Sometimes he croaks like a lonely frog.

But yesterday, asleep in his house,

Little Monkey was as quiet as a mouse.

DIRECTIONS |||| **Complete the following similes.**

1. He was as funny as _____.

2. She was as pretty as _____.

3. The man laughed like _____.

4. The dog was as friendly as _____.

5. The rain on the roof sounded like _____.

✐✐✐ **MORE TO DO** ✐✐✐

With a partner, write five similes. Make up the first part of the simile. For example, you might write, "The wet cat smelled like _____." Then, both of you should fill in the last part of the similes. Draw a picture to go with each simile. When you are finished, share your similes with your classmates.

Finding Metaphors

Another figure of speech is the **metaphor**. A metaphor is also a comparison of two things that are not usually considered alike. This type of comparison, though, does <u>not</u> use the words *like* or *as*. For example, "My room is a garbage can." This does not say the room is <u>like</u> a garbage can, but that the room <u>is</u> a garbage can. The metaphor does not mean that the person lives in a garbage can. The person's room is just very messy, as a garbage can is.

Metaphors are harder to find than similes. Metaphors do not use the signal words *like* or *as*. Sometimes the metaphor will use the word *is*. Sometimes the metaphor has no signal word. For example, "The ship plows the seas" is a metaphor. The ship is compared to a plow. The ship moving through the waves is like a plow moving through the rows of plowed earth.

| DIRECTIONS |||| **Underline the metaphors in the following poem. Then, answer the questions.**

The Moon's the North Wind's Cooky
(What the Little Girl Said)
by Vachel Lindsay

The Moon's the North Wind's cooky,
He bites it day by day,
Until there's but a rim of scraps
That crumble all away.

The South Wind is a baker.
He kneads clouds in his den,
And bakes a crisp new Moon *that ... greedy North ... Wind ... eats ... again*!

1. How many metaphors did you find? _____

2. In the first metaphor, what two things are being compared? _____

_____

3. In the second metaphor, what two things are being compared? _____

_____

4. What event is the poet describing by using these metaphors? _____

_____

Some Little Riddles

Homographs are words that have the same spelling but different meanings. Sometimes homographs have different pronunciations.

We saw a <u>seal</u> at the zoo.
Be sure you <u>seal</u> the envelope before you mail it.

Some animals <u>live</u> on land and in water.
<u>Live</u> plants are not allowed in this building.

DIRECTIONS |||| **Read each riddle. Tell what the underlined word means in each riddle. Then, write a sentence to show a different meaning for each underlined word.**

1. Question: What never comes up when you are <u>down</u>?
Answer: your smile

Meaning: _____

Your sentence: _____

_____

2. Question: How do you fix a pumpkin?
Answer: with a pumpkin <u>patch</u>

Meaning: _____

Your sentence: _____

_____

3. Question: Why did the farmer call his pig Ink?
Answer: because it always kept running out of the <u>pen</u>

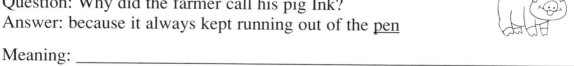

Meaning: _____

Your sentence: _____

_____

✏✏✏ **MOOR TO DEW** ✏✏✏
Make up your own riddles using homographs. Share your riddles with your classmates. Can they answer the riddles?

Home on the Range

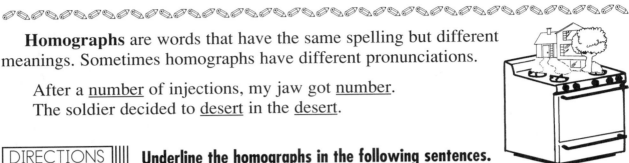

Homographs are words that have the same spelling but different meanings. Sometimes homographs have different pronunciations.

After a <u>number</u> of injections, my jaw got <u>number</u>.
The soldier decided to <u>desert</u> in the <u>desert</u>.

| DIRECTIONS ||||| **Underline the homographs in the following sentences.**

1. We must polish the Polish furniture.

2. A bass was painted on the head of the bass drum.

3. I did not object to the object.

4. The dump was so full that it had to refuse more refuse.

5. The bandage was wound around the wound.

| DIRECTIONS ||||| **Underline the homographs in the following sentences. Then, rewrite each sentence using synonyms for the homographs.**

6. They were too close to the door to close it. _____

_____

7. The wind was too strong to wind the sail. _____

_____

8. Upon seeing the tear in my clothes, I shed a tear. _____

_____

9. The farm was used to produce produce. _____

_____

10. This was a good time to present the present. _____

_____

✐✎✐ **MOOR TO DEW** ✎✐✎
Write your own sentence using homographs. Draw a picture to show the different meanings of the homographs you use.

Wears the Homophone?

Homophones are words that sound the same but are spelled differently. They also have different meanings. *Blue* and *blew* are homophones. If you write the wrong homophone, you may not be saying what you really mean.

| DIRECTIONS ||| **Read each sentence below. Find each homophone that is used incorrectly. Underline it. Then, rewrite the sentences using the correct words.**

1. Do you no how to go to the library? _____
_____

2. No won is aloud to talk during a fire drill. _____
_____

3. Wee are studying sells in hour science class. _____
_____

4. Cecile red a book of tall tails. _____
_____

5. We looked at the beautiful neckless in the store window. _____
_____

6. The night wore a knew suit of armor. _____
_____

7. When I am board, I right poems. _____
_____

✐✐✐ **MOOR TO DEW** ✐✐✐

Write five sentences that use homophones incorrectly. Let a classmate find the homophones. Then, the classmate should rewrite your sentences using the correct words. For extra fun, draw a picture that illustrates one of the incorrect sentences.

Homophone Riddles

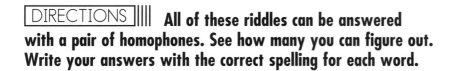

Homophones are words that sound the same but are spelled differently. They also have different meanings. *Where* and *wear* are homophones. Writers can make riddles by using homophones.

Question: What means "see the camp location"?
Answer: sight site

| DIRECTIONS ||| **All of these riddles can be answered with a pair of homophones. See how many you can figure out. Write your answers with the correct spelling for each word.**

1. Question: What do you call an animal with a sore throat?

Answer: _____

2. Question: What do you call a rose made of wheat?

Answer: _____

3. Question: What do you call time that belongs to us?

Answer: _____

4. Question: What do you call a vendor of space under a building?

Answer: _____

5. Question: What do you call an underage coal digger?

Answer: _____

 **MOOR TO DEW**

Use homophones to make up your own riddles. See if your classmates can guess your riddles.

Hears Sum Homophones

Homophones are words that sound the same but are spelled differently. They also have different meanings. *Here* and *hear* are homophones. Writers can have fun by using homophones.

| DIRECTIONS ||| **Read the following poem. Circle all the homophones the poet has used.**

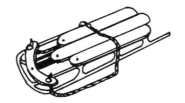

A Misspelled Tail
by Elizabeth T. Corbett

A little buoy said, "Mother, deer,
   May I go out too play?
The son is bright, the heir is clear,
   Owe, mother, don't say neigh!"

"Go fourth, my sun," the mother said.
   The ant said, "Take ewer slay,
Your gneiss knew sled, awl painted read,
   Butt dew knot lose your weigh."

"Ah, know," he cried, and sought the street
   With hart sew full of glee—
The whether changed—and snow and sleet,
   And reign, fell steadily.

Threw snowdrifts grate, threw watery pool,
   He flue with mite and mane—
Said he, "Though I wood walk by rule,
   I am not rite, 'tis plane.

"I'd like to meat sum kindly sole,
   For hear gnu dangers weight,
And yonder stairs a treacherous whole—
   Two sloe has been my gate.

"A peace of bred, a nice hot stake,
   I'd chews if I were home,
This crewel fete my hart will brake,
   Eye love knot thus to roam.

"I'm week and pail, I've mist my rode,"
   But here a carte came past,
He and his sled were safely toad
   Back two his home at last.

✎✎✎ MOOR TO DEW ✎✎✎

Write your own poem that uses homophones. How many homophones can you think of? See if your classmates can find all the homophones in your poem.

Unit Three: Enrichment
Figurative Language 4, SV 2718-9

Having Fun with Homophones

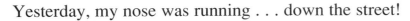

Some words are spelled and written the same way, but they mean different things. These words are called **homographs**. *Homo* means "same," and *graph* means "write." *Ball*, meaning "a game toy," and *ball*, meaning "a fancy dance," are homographs.

Some words sound alike, but they are spelled differently. They also mean different things. These words are called **homophones**. *Phone* means "sound." *Sun* and *son* are homophones.

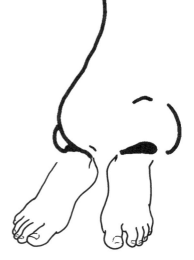

You can make up funny jokes by using homographs or homophones. These jokes are sometimes called **wordplays** or **puns**. Here are some examples:

Yesterday, my nose was running . . . down the street!

I taught my dog to heel . . . and now he's a doctor in Roverville!

| DIRECTIONS | |||| **Underline the homograph or homophone in each sentence.**

1. Did you ever hear Aesop's fable of the tortoise and the hair?

2. I went to the ocean and saw a wail.

3. Did you hear about the girl who went to the cosmetics store to take a makeup test?

4. Did you hear about the race between the lettuce and the tomato? The lettuce was a head, and the tomato was trying to catch up.

5. Seven days in bed makes one weak.

✏️✏️✏️ MOOR TO DEW ✏️✏️✏️

Write your own funny lines using homophones. Underline the word or group of words that makes the wordplay.

More Jokes

Many jokes use homographs and homophones. The wordplays can be very funny. See how this joke uses a homophone.

Question: If you were stranded in a desert, how could you survive?

Answer: You could eat the sand which is (sandwiches) there.

DIRECTIONS |||| **Here are some more jokes. Share them with your friends.**

1. Why did the chicken cross the playground? (To get to the other slide)

2. What gets bigger and smaller the more you take away from it? (A hole/whole)

3. Why did Little Monkey take a ruler to bed? (To see how long he slept)

4. What kind of dog is best able to keep time? (A watch dog)

5. What do you call a butcher's dance? (A meatball)

6. What kind of wood should you use to build a cow shed? (Cattle logs)

7. When is a car not a car? (When it turns into a driveway)

8. What did the baby corn call its father? (Pop Corn)

9. Little Monkey and Bob Baboon were talking. "All my hair is falling out," said Bob Baboon. "Do you know something I can get to keep it in?" "A paper bag," said Little Monkey.

 MOOR TO DEW ✏✏✏
Make up your own jokes using homographs and homophones. Tell your jokes to your classmates. Have a contest to see who has the funniest jokes.

Poetry Fun

Now that you know all about figurative language and poems, you are ready to write some good poems. Think carefully about the words you use in your poems. Try to use all the poet's tools to make your poem better.

DIRECTIONS ▕▏▏▏ **Use the activities below to help you write.**

1. With a partner, find a picture of a pretty scene in a magazine. Each of you should write five similes or metaphors that describe the picture. Choose the six best similes or metaphors. Cut out the picture, and paste it at the top of a piece of paper. Under the picture, use the six chosen similes or metaphors to write a poem about the picture.

2. Write a song that has rhyming words. Sing the song for your class.

3. Use alliteration to write a tongue-twister poem. Here's an example:

Peter Piper picked a peck of pickled peppers.
A peck of pickled peppers Peter Piper picked.
If Peter Piper picked a peck of pickled peppers,
Where's the peck of pickled peppers Peter Piper picked?

4. With a partner, write a poem that rhymes. Make up five sets of rhymes. If you can't think of any rhymes, try these: blue/new; bed/bread; go/snow; bright/white; dog/log. You should choose one of the words in each set. Your partner gets the other word in each set. Then, each of you should write lines for your poem that end with the rhyming words. Finally, write out the poem, using the lines written by both partners. Arrange the lines any way you like. You have poetic license!